11+
English
Spelling & Vocabulary

Foundation Level
WORKBOOK 3

Dr Stephen C Curran

with Warren Vokes

Edited by Mark Schofield

This book belongs to

Accelerated Education Publications Ltd.

window	broom	yard
card	garden	bedroom
shade	spade	barn
harm	farm	less

Exercise 47a

1) The cows had walked along the road to the __farm__ and left it very muddy.

2) It was _____ a long way to the shops that she had to catch a bus.

3) She sat at the mirror in her _____ to comb her hair.

4) The toys were left outside but it did not rain and they came to no _____ .

5) It was over thirty degrees in the _____ and far too hot to play tennis.

6) He could feel the _____ from the fire from across the room.

7) A very _____ pile of magazines had been stacked on the coffee table.

8) With the lawn mown and trimmed the _____ looked very tidy.

9) She broke the eggs into a bowl and then _____ them with a whisk.

10) "_____ you," she said as he sneezed for the second time.

Score | 10

Exercise 47b

11) I asked the price and it was much _____ than I had expected.

12) "Close the _____ , there's a draught in here."

13) "_____ the green button and the gate will open."

14) The _____ was selling newly laid eggs and she bought two dozen.

15) The salesman gave his business _____ to the receptionist.

16) Chickens roamed freely around the _____ at the back of the farmhouse.

17) Harvest was over and the _____ was full with bales of hay.

18) She used the garden _____ to sweep the fallen leaves from the patio.

19) Vegetarians don't eat _____ .

20) He couldn't wait to use his bucket and _____ on the beach.

Score | 10

© 2006 Stephen Curran

bless	press
meat	heat
beat	neat
such	farmer

Word Bank TOTAL 940

Across

3. Enclosed paved piece of land.
5. Brush for sweeping.
6. Agricultural land and buildings.
7. Large farm outbuilding used for storage.
10. Cultivated area around a house.
11. Damage or injury.
12. Digging tool with handle and wide blade.
14. So much.
15. Smaller amount.
16. Glass covered opening in a building.
17. To hit repeatedly.

Down

1. Stiff paper with pictures and greetings.
2. Owner or operator of a farm.
4. A room for sleeping.
7. To make holy.
8. To push against something.
9. Edible animal flesh.
11. Energy felt as warmth or hotness.
12. Area out of direct sunlight.
13. Orderly in appearance.

47

Put the mystery letter (✳) into the box marked **47** below. Add in the mystery letters from puzzles **48** to **54** then rearrange them to make **Kate's Mystery Word**.

The clue is **ANIMAL**.

3 Y A R D

47	48	49	50	51	52	53	54

Enter your mystery letters here:

Now rearrange them:

Mystery Word:

Mystery Letter   Score
                  20

ae © 2006 Stephen Curran

3

fear	clear	heard
pass	class	glass
town	brown	flower
belt	leaf	bunch

Across

48

1. A strip of material around the waist.
4. Perceived sounds.
5. Transparent.
6. Feeling of anxiety caused by danger.
7. Compass point opposite west.
9. Overtake.
11. A large animal.
13. The coloured part of a plant.
14. Flat green part of a plant or tree.
15. Pale reddish colour.

Down

1. Collection of things grouped or joined together.
2. Transparent solid substance used to make bottles, windows and lenses.
3. A group taught together.

Down (continued)

6. A meal for many people to celebrate an occasion.
8. Densely populated area with many buildings.
9. A bucket.
10. Large piece of fabric used on a boat to catch the wind.
11. Colour made from red and green.
12. To use the mind to form thoughts.
13. Level and horizontal without any slope.

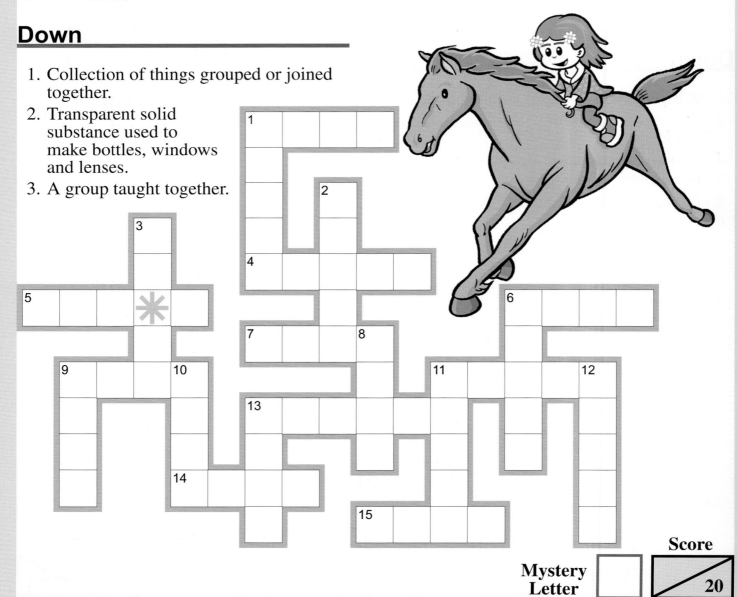

Mystery Letter

Score /20

© 2006 Stephen Curran ae

pink	think	
flat	east	
feast	beast	
sail	pail	

Exercise 48a

1) He was really frightened and the _____ could be seen on his face.

2) The newspapers referred to the animal as the '_____ *of Bodmin Moor'*.

3) It was a large _____ of flowers that she had picked that morning.

4) The _____ autumn leaves that had fallen from the trees littered the streets.

5) The albino rabbit's nose was very _____ and his fur was pure white.

6) The window had been broken and pieces of _____ were lying on the ground.

7) The driver _____ the guard's whistle, saw the green flag and released the brake.

8) "Could you please _____ me the cruet. I would like some pepper on my meal."

9) Through the _____ water of the stream he saw the fish swimming past.

10) The _____ had been eaten by the caterpillars.

Score / 10

Exercise 48b

11) Their _____ went on a school journey to the science museum.

12) The ship headed _____ as the sun sank below the horizon behind its stern.

13) It was market day and the _____ was full of people looking for a bargain.

14) "Make sure you always wear your seat _____ when travelling in the car."

15) The earth was believed to be _____ before it was circumnavigated.

16) All the plants were beginning to _____ in the warm sunshine.

17) The wind picked up and the yacht's _____ billowed out as it gathered speed.

18) I didn't _____ anybody had heard me but help arrived soon after I called out.

19) A huge _____ was held in the great hall to celebrate their success.

20) He used the metal _____ to fetch water for the animals.

Score / 10

ae © 2006 Stephen Curran

5

nail	fail	mix
least	lame	blame
tame	drill	spill
spell	cream	dream

Exercise 49a

1) The horse had gone _____ and he had to dismount and walk instead.

2) After using this book he found that he was _____ all the words correctly.

3) The pneumatic _____ that they were using to dig up the road was very loud.

4) It was only a _____ and when he awoke there was no one else in the room.

5) Apple _____ was his favourite dessert but for a change he ordered the gâteau.

6) The rabbit was very _____ and liked children holding and stroking it.

7) She could not _____ to be noticed wearing such a huge wide-brimmed hat.

8) "The _____ you could do is offer to help clear up your mess!"

9) "I didn't mean to _____ my drink. It was an accident!"

10) "It was your fault and you must take the _____ ."

Score [/ 10]

Exercise 49b

11) "Make sure you water the plants or they will _____ in this heat."

12) He had been caught and hung his head in _____ as they led him away.

13) He hung his jacket on an old rusty _____ which stuck out from the door.

14) "Would you like some _____ with your strawberries?" the waiter asked.

15) After they had finished the _____ he asked the waiter for the bill.

16) The wicked witch cast her evil _____ on the beautiful princess.

17) It was a _____ when he said he had not seen them. He'd spoken to them before they left.

18) Our hotel swimming _____ was very crowded so we went to the beach instead.

19) "Here, _____ this pastille. It will help to soothe your sore throat."

20) The pancake _____ contained flour, eggs and milk.

Score [/ 10]

© 2006 Stephen Curran

meal	spelling
shame	suck
die	pie
lie	pool

Word Bank TOTAL 980

Across

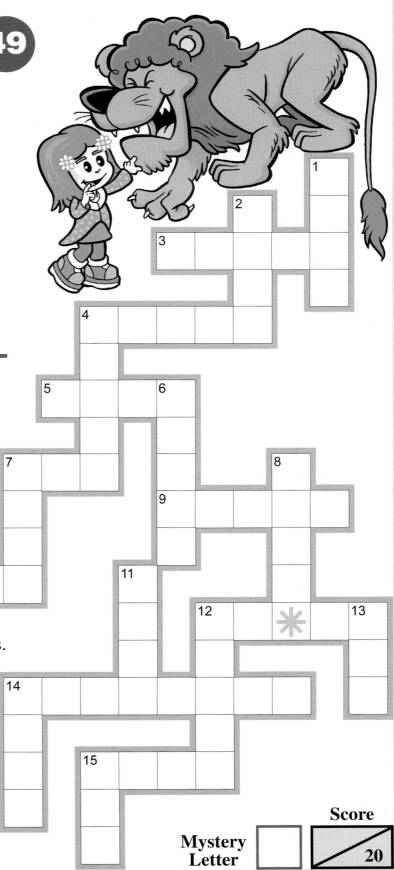

49

3. The fatty part of milk.
4. To name or write in correct order the letters of a word.
5. To be unsuccessful.
7. To deliberately say something untrue.
9. Accidentally allow something to flow from a container.
10. To stop living.
12. Images that appear to the mind while asleep.
14. Forming words with letters.
15. A small body of still water.

Down

1. No longer wild.
2. A substantial amount of food eaten at one time.
4. A state of disgrace or dishonour.
6. The smallest amount possible.
7. Walking unevenly because of a leg injury.
8. To consider somebody responsible for something wrong that has happened.
11. Strong pointed metal pin hammered into wood or masonry.
12. Rotating piece of metal that bores holes.
13. To combine ingredients.
14. To draw liquid out with the mouth.
15. Baked dish consisting of a filling enclosed in or covered with pastry.

Mystery Letter

Score / 20

ae © 2006 Stephen Curran

cool	food	turn
burn	hurt	lies
church	curl	oak
goat	load	ready

Across

50

1. A substance, normally solid, providing nourishment.
4. Coldish. Usually pleasantly so.
7. To cause pain.
8. To move to face a different direction.
10. A polite form of address to a man.
11. A tree bearing acorns as fruit.
12. An article of clothing for the upper body.
14. Ceased to exist.
17. Something heavy or bulky carried or transported.
18. The end of being alive.

Down

1. Compact and solid when pressed.
2. An unclean substance.
3. To be or to set on fire.
4. To bend, twist or wind something into a curved or spiral shape.
5. False statements made deliberately.
6. A building for public worship.
9. Prepared for something that is going to happen.
13. One of three equal parts.
15. No longer alive.
16. A horned mammal related to sheep.

Mystery Letter

Score

20

8

© 2006 Stephen Curran

dead   death
sir   dirt
firm   shirt
third   died

Exercise 50a

1) Following the _____ of the king, his eldest son acceded to the throne.

2) "Please _____ , may I leave the classroom?" he asked the teacher.

3) The squirrel was collecting acorns from the _____ tree to store for the winter.

4) The forest fire continued to _____ and they could only hope it would soon rain.

5) They were so well matched they crossed the line together in a _____ heat.

6) He was being collected at seven o'clock but he was _____ long before.

7) It is customary for the bride to arrive at the _____ late for her wedding.

8) The auctioneer asked for the _____ and last time and banged his gavel. "Sold!"

9) The fan helped to keep them _____ in the hot weather.

10) "The collar on this new _____ is making my neck sore."   **Score** /10

Exercise 50b

11) "Could you help me _____ these suitcases onto the roof rack?"

12) An old nanny _____ was chained to a stake at the edge of the field.

13) When he got to his feet he brushed the _____ from the knees of his trousers.

14) He took the free kick and managed to _____ the ball around the goalkeeper.

15) "The place you want _____ at the foot of those hills you can see over there."

16) " _____ again Whittington, Lord Mayor of London."

17) The hotel bed was very _____ and he preferred a softer mattress.

18) Her pet hamster had _____ and her parents took her to buy another one.

19) The rugby player wrenched his knee and it _____ when he stood up.

20) The favourite _____ of the giant panda is bamboo shoots.   **Score** /10

ae © 2006 Stephen Curran

9

air	pair	stair
night	right	bright
word	world	forget
upstairs	downstairs	tonight

Exercise 51a

1) The _____ was high in the tree and its caw could be heard across the landscape.

2) The north _____ shines brighter than the rest and is easy to identify.

3) The windows in the rooms _____ overlooked the garden next door.

4) It was a _____ bridge and the lorry had struck the brickwork and become stuck.

5) They went _____ , closed the door and waited for it to stop raining.

6) It was a cold, wet _____ and they longed for the warmth of the morning sun.

7) There was a _____ of brass candlesticks for sale in the antique shop.

8) "Don't _____ to send me a postcard from Cyprus when you are away."

9) They made very _____ progress along the steep and muddy path.

10) The cannon fired to signal the _____ of the yacht race.

Score [/ 10]

Exercise 51b

11) I can't decide whether to see the matinée or go to _____ 's performance.

12) The weather _____ was atrocious and they decided to stay indoors.

13) The _____ tread creaked when he placed his foot on it.

14) "Write down this _____ , look it up in the dictionary and tell me its meaning."

15) He heard a sound in the night and went _____ to investigate.

16) The car turned _____ at the crossroads and headed away from the town centre.

17) The _____ was leaking from the tyre and it was slowly deflating.

18) Sir Francis Chichester was the first lone yachtsman to sail around the _____ .

19) "All burglaries must be reported to the police _____ 24 hours."

20) "His is a very _____ pupil and should do well here."

Score [/ 10]

© 2006 Stephen Curran

inside	outside
within	low
slow	crow
star	start

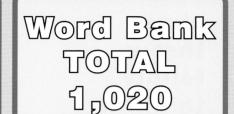

Word Bank TOTAL 1,020

Across

51

1. Earth and everything on it.
4. Not moving quickly.
6. The internal part of something.
9. Large bird with shiny black feathers and a raucous cry.
11. Giving off strong light.
12. A flight of steps leading from one level to another.
15. Two matching objects that are designed to be used together.
16. The night or evening of the present day.
17. To, towards, or on an upper level.
20. Unit of language either spoken or written.

Down

2. To, towards, or on a lower level.
3. The mixture of gases that forms the Earth's atmosphere.
5. Close to the ground.
7. The entire period between sunset and sunrise.
8. To fail to remember something.
10. The outer surface or appearance of something.
13. The east when facing north.
14. Somebody or something is inside.
18. Point of light in the night sky.
19. To begin.

Mystery Letter

Score /20

© 2006 Stephen Curran

sharp	without	own
throw	bow	row
follow	walking	talking
thinking	walked	talked

Across

52

2. Used to ask about the reason, cause or purpose of something.
4. To have something as property.
5. To go after somebody.
8. Not having or not accompanied by.
10. Speaking.
13. Weapon for firing arrows.
16. Requested.
17. Moving on foot.
18. Travelled on foot.
19. One of a range of things.

Down

1. Propel something from the hand.
3. A line of things.
6. Using the eyes to search.
7. Able to cut.
9. Forming thoughts in the mind.
11. Turned the eyes towards something.
12. Neither.
14. Woman servant.
15. Had a conversation.
18. Introduction to a question about the name of a person.

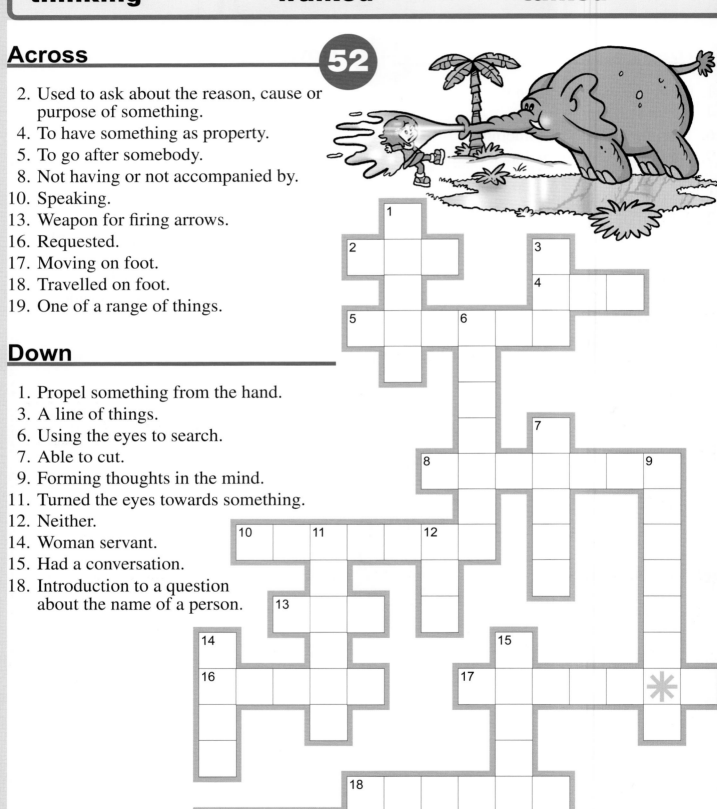

Score

Mystery Letter

20

12

© 2006 Stephen Curran   ae

Exercise 52a

1) "Do you know _____ left that there for us to trip over?" asked the headmaster.

2) Neither the workman _____ the lorry driver could find the wheelbarrow.

3) The cars were parked in a _____ that was at least 10 metres long.

4) The audience continued to applaud and the cast took another _____ .

5) They had a lot of news for each other and they _____ for ages.

6) They _____ slowly along the river bank studying the water fowl.

7) He rang for the _____ and asked her to bring them tea and cakes.

8) "Don't _____ sand at each other. It will get in your eyes!"

9) I was not clear _____ the signal had failed to operate.

10) My cat was sitting on the window sill _____ at the birds.

Score ◸ 10

Exercise 52b

11) I spent many hours _____ to the old man about his life on the canals.

12) He had entered _____ permission and was arrested for trespassing.

13) He had been _____ for many hours before he came to the village.

14) "Try to complete the exercises on your _____ but ask me if you need help."

15) It _____ certain that they would win but then they conceded a goal.

16) She had _____ for black coffee but it came with milk.

17) The blade was very _____ and it cut through the rope with ease.

18) She was not sure _____ blouse to buy as she liked them both.

19) "I was _____ I might call in and see you as I'm passing."

20) We tried to _____ the path but it became very overgrown.

Score ◸ 10

doctor	fork	speak
speaking	reading	pork
trip	whip	opening
opened	washed	alive

Exercise 53a

1) After the heavy rainfall the water butt was _____ to overflowing.

2) The _____ chops in the butcher's window looked very good value.

3) A large black _____ passed overhead and obscured the sun.

4) Despite being very ill the sick animal was still _____ the following day.

5) It was a very cold _____ wind that blew down from the arctic circle.

6) There was a small _____ in the hedge which he could just squeeze through.

7) He could see the cows were gathered all _____ the edge of the field.

8) "Mind where you walk and don't _____ over that tree stump in the ground."

9) She rang the _____ 's surgery to make an appointment.

10) "Please could you _____ louder, I'm a little deaf."

Score 10

Exercise 53b

11) The standard unit of currency in _____ Africa is the rand.

12) They had turned the wrong way at the _____ in the road.

13) Her appointment was three o'clock but an _____ later she had still not been seen.

14) "That music is far too _____ ; please could you turn it down."

15) It was a secret and they were _____ to each other very quietly.

16) She was sitting in her favourite chair _____ another chapter from the novel.

17) He _____ aware of a sound behind him, turned and saw them approaching.

18) She had _____ her skirt several times but the stain refused to come out.

19) The jockey used his _____ to drive the horse on towards the finish.

20) The door _____ onto a small patio that faced due south.

Score 10

© 2006 Stephen Curran ae

Across

53

2. The flesh of a pig eaten as food.
4. A thin strip of leather attached to a handle.
6. In a particular direction.
8. Involving speech.
10. Living and not dead.
11. 60 minutes.
13. One of the cardinal points on a compass.
15. Somebody qualified to give medical treatment.
16. Changed or developed.
17. A mass of water particles in the sky.
19. Identifying written words.

Down

1. Utter words.
3. A gap.
5. A journey.
7. Cleaned with water.
8. Compass point opposite north.

Down (continued)

9. Took up all the space.
12. Eating utensil with prongs.
14. Not closed or locked.
18. High in volume or sound.

Mystery Letter

Score / 20

ae © 2006 Stephen Curran

15

playground	**football**	**march**
master	**basket**	**tiny**
babies	**ladies**	**stories**
new	**party**	**dance**

Exercise 54a

1) The old sailor told incredible _____ about his exploits at sea.

2) He had lost most of his _____ and had great difficulty chewing.

3) Only one broken, yellowing _____ remained at the front of his mouth.

4) The maternity ward was full of new _____ and the sound of their crying.

5) The small boy would _____ up and down and pretend to be a soldier.

6) It was a fine day and perfect weather for playing cricket on the village _____ .

7) It was too wet to go out into the _____ so we had to stay in school.

8) England won the international _____ match against France by two goals.

9) She had a warm, relaxing _____ and went to bed early.

10) He was _____ his hair cut at the barber's.

Score 10

Exercise 54b

11) "Your worship the Mayor, _____ and gentlemen. Good evening to you all."

12) I asked him but he was _____ nothing away and ignored my question.

13) They hadn't _____ each other for many years but he still recognised her.

14) The highlight of Jennifer's birthday was the _____ in the evening.

15) It was a very grand house and had a huge _____ bedroom.

16) We sat on the sofa in the _____ room and opened the photograph album.

17) It was just like _____ and sparkled in the bright lights of the shop window.

18) He looked down at her. Compared with his own, the little baby's hand was _____ .

19) The *Charleston* was a _____ that was all the rage in the 1920s.

20) She was frail and used a shopping _____ with wheels.

Score 10

© 2006 Stephen Curran

having	giving
living	tooth
teeth	bath
seen	green

Word Bank TOTAL 1,080

Across

54

2. Passing something to somebody.
3. A social gathering for fun.
7. Game played by kicking or heading a round ball.
10. Walk in military fashion.
12. Short works of fiction.
15. A colour between yellow and blue.
16. Recently made.
17. Large container to sit in and wash your body.
18. Man in position of authority.
19. A series of rhythmical steps and body movements.

Down

1. Extremely small.
4. White bony object in the mouth.
5. Women.

Down (continued)

6. Possessing or owning.
8. Alive, not dead.
9. Very young children who cannot yet walk or talk.
11. Outdoor play area with swings, slides and seesaws.
13. Used for biting and chewing food.
14. Examined, looked at or watched using the eyes.
17. A woven container with a handle.

! Don't forget to go back to page **3** and complete **Kate's Mystery Word**.

Mystery Letter

Score / 20

ae © 2006 Stephen Curran

At the Office

Can you find all these words in the picture below? Write the correct word against each number.

chart	swivel chair	desk lamp	bin	extinguisher
fan	lift	manager	pot plant	blind
briefcase	first aid kit	skyscraper	report	secretary

1._____ 2._____ 3._____

4._____ 5._____ 6._____

7._____ 8._____ 9._____

10._____ 11._____ 12._____

13._____ 14._____ 15._____

© 2006 Stephen Curran

In the Street

Can you find all these words in the picture below? Write the correct word against each number. When you have finished you can colour in the picture if you want to.

wall	hedge	bungalow	aerial	bicycle
removal lorry	roof	flower bed	garage	carport
chimney	'Sold' board	lamp post	motor scooter	shed

1._____ 2._____ 3._____

4._____ 5._____ 6._____

7._____ 8._____ 9._____

10._____ 11._____ 12._____

13._____ 14._____ 15._____

© 2006 Stephen Curran

feel	**riding**	**heel**
once	**cherry**	**cherries**
berries	**jelly**	**jolly**
tomorrow	**carry**	**carried**

Exercise 55a

1) There was a thorn in the dog's _____ and the vet had to remove it.

2) I prefer _____ my bicycle to school than going by bus.

3) My mother found an old _____ mould shaped like a rabbit in a charity shop.

4) His legs really ached but he _____ on running, determined to win.

5) Curry with _____ is one of my favourite meals.

6) As we cannot go today, I have arranged to go out _____ with my brother.

7) "A very _____ Christmas to you all!" he cried.

8) The paint she had chosen for the garage door was a bright _____ red.

9) I gave her a pound and she gave me nineteen _____ change.

10) Joshua struggled to _____ his heavy bag to school.   **Score** ☐ 10

Exercise 55b

11) "Look at the birds stripping the _____ from the shrubs to eat."

12) Her shoe got caught in a drain and the high _____ was ripped off.

13) "I expect I _____ see you again at the club meeting next week."

14) Only one mouse was white, the other _____ were brown.

15) He was very embarrassed and did not _____ that he deserved such praise.

16) The man was very friendly with a _____ face and big red cheeks.

17) She only needed to be shown _____ and she could do it for herself.

18) My dad told me that he asked my mum to _____ him when they were only eighteen.

19) A fruit bowl full of shiny red _____ stood on the sideboard.

20) A _____ is a small, juicy fruit.   **Score** ☐ 10

© 2006 Stephen Curran

shall	berry
merry	marry
rice	mice
pence	paw

Word Bank TOTAL 1,100

Across

55

1. Intended to happen.
4. Friendly and cheerful.
7. Small, round fruit with a single hard stone.
8. To take somebody in marriage.
11. Edible grains from the plant of the same name served hot or cold after cooking in water.
13. Being on a horse.
14. A four-legged animal's foot.
15. Touch something.
16. More than one cherry.
17. Small rodents with a brown or greyish-brown coat and a long hairless tail.

Down

2. Back part of the foot.
3. To hold and transport.
4. A wobbly fruit flavoured dessert.
5. Small, juicy, fleshy fruit.
6. The next day.
7. Taken to another place.
9. Lively and cheerful.
10. Any small juicy fruits.
12. At a time in the past.
14. Term for the unit of money used in Britain since 1971.

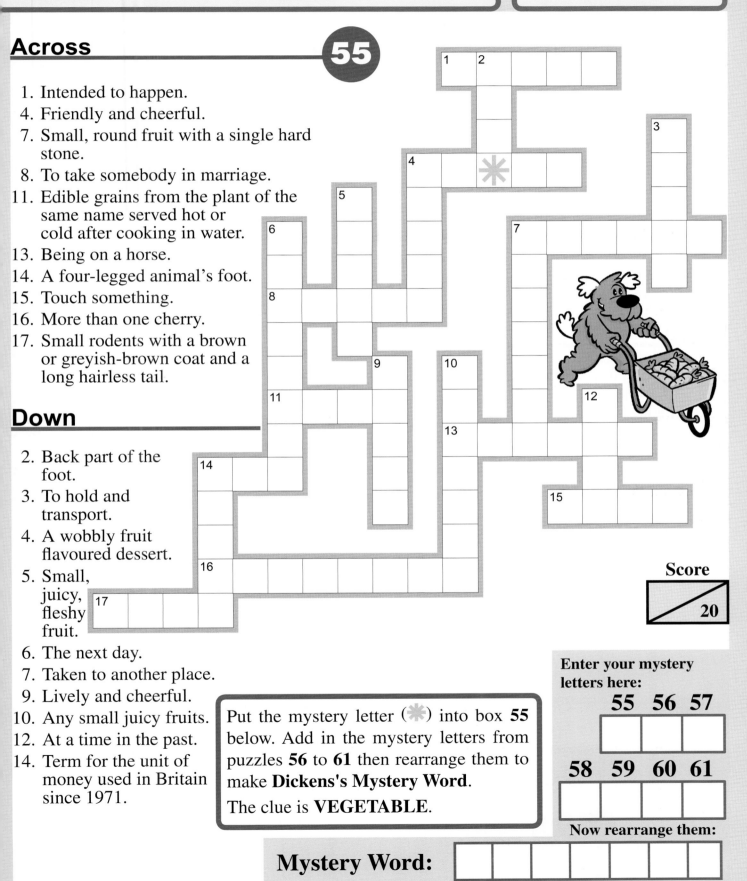

Score / 20

Put the mystery letter (✳) into box **55** below. Add in the mystery letters from puzzles **56** to **61** then rearrange them to make **Dickens's Mystery Word**.
The clue is **VEGETABLE**.

Enter your mystery letters here:

55	56	57

58	59	60	61

Now rearrange them:

Mystery Word:

ae © 2006 Stephen Curran

raw	draw	bean
lean	mean	lead
beads	gay	crying
cried	tried	flies

Across

56

4. A plant with edible pods and seeds.
5. To give pleasure or satisfaction to somebody.
8. Not difficult.
9. Shedding tears.
13. Conducts a legal case in court.
14. To go ahead and show the way.
15. To stretch out or extend as far as a particular point.
16. Attempted.
18. To make a picture.

Down

1. Unwilling to spend money on other people.
2. Quite hot.
3. Travels in an aircraft.
4. A strip of sand or pebbles at the point where the land meets the sea.

Down (continued)

6. Without excess fat.
7. Brightly coloured.
9. Makes a distinctive sound.
10. Very large and impressive.
11. Called out loudly.
12. Spheres pierced for stringing on a necklace.
17. Uncooked.

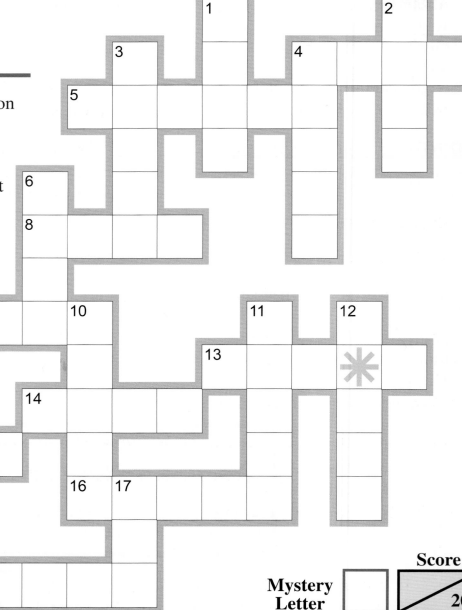

Mystery Letter

Score

/20

© 2006 Stephen Curran

cries	tries
beach	reach
easy	warm
please	great

Exercise 56a

1) By standing on a chair he could just _____ the top of the cupboard.

2) The meat was very undercooked and almost _____ so he sent it back.

3) The street looked very _____ with brightly coloured bunting and flags.

4) He has his own light aircraft and _____ to Le Tourquet every weekend.

5) She did all she could to _____ him but he still found fault with her.

6) My sister is really _____ ; she won't share her sweets with me.

7) Simon found the test quite _____ but Jason found it difficult.

8) Her necklace broke and the _____ fell to the ground and went everywhere.

9) "Let's go to the _____ , it's a lovely day for swimming."

10) Her baby was hungry and _____ for attention.

Score _____ / 10

Exercise 56b

11) The distinctive _____ of hyenas could be heard from far away.

12) The thermos flask had kept the coffee _____ and it tasted very good.

13) "I've really _____ hard to improve but I don't seem to get any better."

14) Around the final bend she took the _____ and went on to win the race.

15) Isambard Kingdom Brunel completed many _____ engineering projects.

16) "I wish I could _____ and paint like my art teacher."

17) We put a _____ onto a wet sheet of kitchen roll and after a few days it sprouted.

18) The bacon rashers were very _____ with hardly any fat at all.

19) Whenever my friend tells a joke he _____ hard not to laugh.

20) The wounded animal was _____ out in pain.

Score _____ / 10

skipping	dropping	running
stopped	dropped	getting
bigger	biggest	better
their	two	slippers

Exercise 57a

1) My dad and I used to go out just _____ dawn to look for mushrooms.

2) He _____ to his knees behind the bushes and raised his binoculars.

3) They arrived on Thursday, _____ days before the weekend.

4) "Fetch my _____ for me and help me take my shoes off," said Granddad.

5) She was _____ really wet and wished she had remembered her umbrella.

6) "Is there _____ I can get for you from the supermarket when I go?"

7) They were all very large but by far the _____ was Brian's.

8) There were not _____ bracelets on display so she asked to see some more.

9) "You look very tired; it's _____ you stay here and rest."

10) Down _____ the ship's hold was full of machinery.

Score | 10

Exercise 57b

11) She enjoyed _____ with her friends turning the rope.

12) She pulled the blanket tighter around her but she still _____ cold.

13) It was September and the conkers were _____ from the horse chestnut trees.

14) My mum always made sure that there was _____ fruit in the bowl for us to eat.

15) He had left the water _____ and the bath was almost overflowing.

16) "Do you have _____ more cornflakes? This box is empty."

17) The blazer did not _____ to anyone there so he handed it in as lost property.

18) The rain had _____ earlier but the grass was still much too wet to cut.

19) It was obvious from the look on _____ faces that they were guilty.

20) I gave the _____ of the two bananas to Rachel.

Score | 10

© 2006 Stephen Curran ae

before belong many fresh

below any anything felt

Word Bank TOTAL 1,140

Across

57

2. A fabric made from wool or animal hair.
4. A considerable number.
6. Every person or thing stated.
8. Belonging to them.
9. Not old or stale.
13. Jumping over a circling rope.
15. Earlier than a particular date, time or event.
16. Bringing or obtaining.
17. Fallen from a higher place.
18. Rapid movement on foot.

Down

1. More pleasing or acceptable.
3. The number 2.
5. Any object, event, action, situation, or fact.
7. Situated or placed beneath something.
10. Came to a standstill.
11. Of greater size, number, or amount.
12. Letting go of something.
13. Flat soft shoes usually worn indoors.
14. To be somebody's property.
15. Of greatest size, number, or amount.

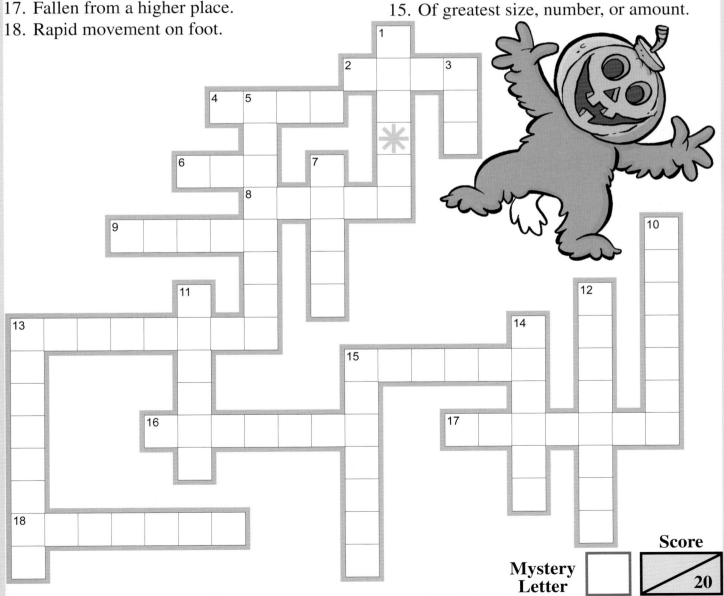

Mystery Letter

Score
/20

ae © 2006 Stephen Curran

melt   nothing   beside
behind   oil   boil
join   few   dew
drew   know   knew

Across

58

4. In a position next to.
5. Tied firmly together.
6. To cause a liquid to reach the temperature at which it turns to gas.
7. Held in your possession.
9. Water droplets on cool outdoor surfaces.
10. Believed firmly.
12. To bring or come together.
13. Indicates separation or distance between two points.
15. Made a picture using a pencil.
16. A zero quantity.

Down

1. At the back or rear.
2. Something that can be heard.
3. To change a substance from a solid to a liquid state by heating it.
5. Moved as a current of air.
8. Unit of currency used in the United Kingdom.
10. To be certain about something.
11. Indicate with an extended finger.
14. Not many.
17. Thick greasy liquid.
18. Became larger.

Mystery Letter

Score

20

26

© 2006 Stephen Curran

grew   blew
off   point
pound   sound
bound   kept

Word Bank TOTAL 1,160

Exercise 58a

1) "Over a low heat, _____ the butter in the omelette pan then add the beaten eggs."

2) Sophie wanted to _____ in the game but she didn't know the rules.

3) He was not very sociable and very much _____ himself to himself.

4) The poacher _____ from experience where to find game to catch illegally.

5) "Something is _____ to turn up," said Mr Macawber.

6) There were only a _____ left and they would not be enough to make a pie.

7) The gate hinges were squeaking but applying the _____ silenced them.

8) The _____ of heavy footsteps echoed down the street and then I saw him!

9) "I know you have it hidden _____ your back. Show me your hands."

10) Somewhere _____ to his left he heard a low whistle.

Score ⊘ 10

Exercise 58b

11) The artillery continued relentlessly to _____ the enemy's position.

12) "Allow the water to come to the _____ before putting in the egg."

13) Without turning his head, he could see she had sat down _____ him.

14) The instructor used a pencil to _____ to the features on the map.

15) He _____ his nose rather loudly and everyone turned towards him.

16) "Do you _____ where they have gone this afternoon? Did they tell you?"

17) The early morning _____ had made his boots wet as he walked across the field.

18) She seized his arm, _____ the boy towards her and whispered softly in his ear.

19) There is _____ more refreshing than a good night's sleep.

Score ⊘ 10

20) The trees _____ to over ten metres high.

ae © 2006 Stephen Curran

desk	key	use
used	puppy	even
ox	oxen	sale
tale	later	learn

Exercise 59a

1) The dog was ill, had lost weight and looked very _____ .

2) Always _____ sun cream to protect you from the effects of ultra violet rays.

3) "See _____ houses over there, I lived in the middle one."

4) There was a tail wind and their flight arrived _____ .

5) The cart was pulled by two _____ led by a young barefoot boy.

6) The water was so clear we _____ see that the bottom was rocky.

7) We used to go to Spain each year and my aunt _____ always come with us.

8) I took my young _____ to dog training lessons to teach it to be obedient.

9) He _____ his time at school to gain all the knowledge he could.

10) It was past six o'clock and much _____ than they thought.   **Score** [/ 10]

Exercise 59b

11) An _____was wearily pulling the plough across the field with a man walking behind.

12) The shop had a _____ to clear all the stock before finally closing down.

13) Sitting at her _____ in the office, the secretary was typing a letter.

14) "Come over here and look at all _____ shells that I have collected."

15) When we changed the lock we had to have several copies of the new _____ cut.

16) Teachers help children to _____ to read and write.

17) "We can _____ to the other side here where the stream is narrower."

18) The current was too _____ and she could not swim against it.

19) She was so forgetful she couldn't _____ remember her son's name.

20) A _____ of Two Cities is a famous novel by Charles Dickens.   **Score** [/ 10]

   © 2006 Stephen Curran ae

early
would
cross
those

strong
could
these
thin

Across

59

1. A story or report that is untrue.
3. Robust and sturdy. Not easily damaged or broken.
6. Angry and upset.
8. Before the expected time.
10. Employ something for some purpose.
12. A time when a shop sells goods at reduced prices.
14. Used when making a polite request or offer.
15. Slim with little body fat.
16. Instrument used for locking and unlocking.
17. Expended or consumed.
18. A table used for work.

Down

2. After the present time.
4. Plural (more than one) of *'that'*.
5. A bovine animal sometimes used for pulling heavy loads and ploughs.
6. Used when making polite requests.
7. Male or female bovine mammals.
9. To come to know something.
11. A dog under a year old.
13. Not sloping, rough, or irregular.
15. Plural (more than one) of *'this'*.

CHILLI'S

Mystery Letter

Score

20

ae © 2006 Stephen Curran

number **ruler** **uncle**
note **woke** **stone**
played **stayed** **clever**
drove **whole** **next**

Across

60

Down

3. Remained.
4. Having the colour of the sky.
6. Showing mental agility and creativity.
8. Following this one.
10. The brother of somebody's mother or father.
12. Something written down as a record or reminder.
13. Finished or completed.
15. Takes action to change a situation or solve a problem.
17. A small piece of rock.
18. Absent after leaving somewhere.

1. Ended their sleep.
2. Took part in a game or sport.
4. Any one of the hard parts forming the skeleton.
5. Unit of length equal to 2.54cm.
7. A tool for measuring and drawing straight lines.
9. Real or correct.
11. Departs.
14. A total or sum.
15. Took somebody somewhere in a vehicle.
16. Complete with nothing left out.

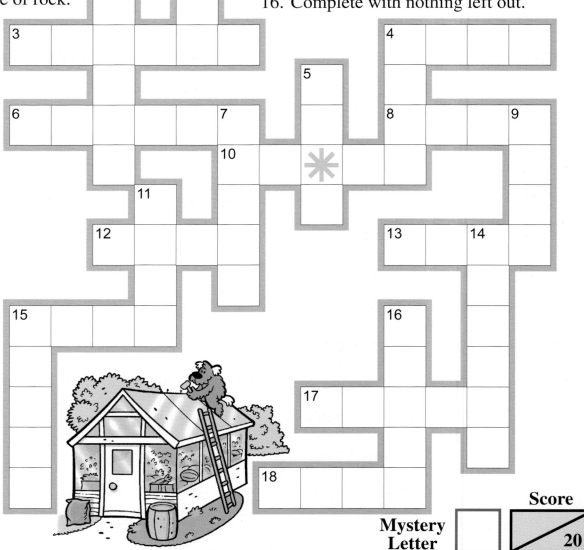

Mystery Letter

Score
/20

© 2006 Stephen Curran

done **gone**
bone **does**
goes **inch**
true **blue**

Word Bank
TOTAL
1,200

Exercise 60a

1) *The* _____ *Danube* is a waltz composed by Johann Strauss, the younger.

2) "At what time _____ your mother usually collect you from school?"

3) The two of them _____ together nicely until she wouldn't share her toy pram.

4) He missed the eight o'clock train and had to wait for the _____ one.

5) When the sun _____ down the evening temperature falls.

6) The imperial measurement of one _____ is equal to just over 2.5 centimetres.

7) We took a picnic and _____ the car out into the countryside.

8) She had left a _____ on the table for her daughter.

9) The note read, " _____ to the shops - will be back within the hour."

10) That evening he _____ in and watched the match.

Score / 10

Exercise 60b

11) Although only a few pupils had misbehaved, the _____ class was punished.

12) Queen Elizabeth I was an able and firm _____ from 1558 until her death in 1603.

13) He had lied before and now she didn't know if anything he told her was _____ .

14) After a restless night, Sheila _____ up tired and irritable.

15) All the _____ used to build St. Paul's Cathedral came from the island of Portland.

16) The femur is the main _____ in the human thigh and is the strongest in the body.

17) "Let's go to the fair. We haven't _____ that for years."

18) Albert Einstein was extremely _____ and a brilliant mathematical physicist.

19) _____ Arthur was the eldest of my father's brothers.

20) There were a _____ of options but none was satisfactory.

Score / 10

silk	some	longer
longest	porridge	arrested
arrived	strawberries	worm
forgets	snore	corridor

Exercise 61a

1) She studied the menu and chose _____ and cream for dessert.

2) Her wedding dress was made from the finest _____ .

3) The cowhand worked on the _____ and slept in the bunkhouse.

4) He always had hot _____ for breakfast in the winter.

5) His cabin was at the end of a narrow _____ on the starboard side.

6) She always _____ his birthday and he has got used to not getting a card.

7) I love the way the skin on his face _____ when he smiles at me.

8) They had _____ , beetroot, spring onions and celery in their salad.

9) He was _____ and taken to the police station to be charged.

10) There was still _____ food left over for later.

Score ⟋ 10

Exercise 61b

11) He was a fine _____ and played many exacting rôles on stage and screen.

12) The _____ I waited the more convinced I became that he was not coming.

13) He insisted he did not _____ while asleep but his wife knew differently.

14) I heard a songbird and the ornithologist confirmed it was a _____ .

15) The _____ river in the United States of America is the Missouri.

16) We finally _____ at our destination after an 11 hour journey.

17) The *Titanic* struck an _____ and sank on her maiden voyage in 1912.

18) I watched the blackbird pull the long _____ from the soil.

19) The worm continued to _____ in its beak as the bird flew off.

20) Hirohito was the _____ of Japan during World War II.

Score ⟋ 10

© 2006 Stephen Curran æ

actor　　　　**emperor**
wrinkles　　　**wriggle**
iceberg　　　**lettuce**
finch　　　　**ranch**

**Word Bank
TOTAL
1,220**

Across

61

2. Lines or creases in the skin that form on the face.
4. To breathe noisily when asleep.
6. A little or quite a few.
8. A livestock farm on open land in North and South America and Australia.
10. A performer in plays on stage, in films and on television.
12. With a greater length.
13. The ruler of an empire.
14. The thread from silkworms and fabric made from it.
16. To twist and turn.
17. An invertebrate with a slender, soft, cylindrical or flat body.
18. Hot breakfast cereal made from oatmeal.

Down

1. Stopped, or taken into custody.
3. A passage inside a building.
5. A plant with edible leaves usually eaten in salads.
7. Does not remember.
9. A small songbird.
10. Reached a place having come from another place.
11. Edible heart-shaped red fruit.
12. With the greatest length.
15. A mass of ice floating in the sea.

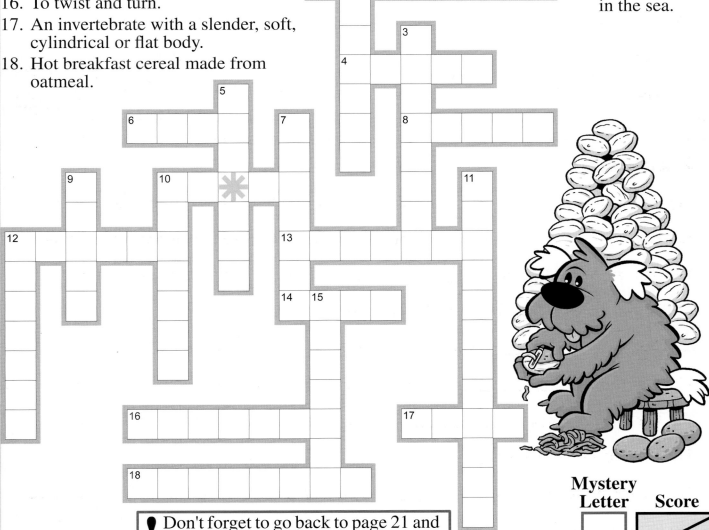

Mystery Letter 　 **Score**

20

! Don't forget to go back to page 21 and complete **Dickens's Mystery Word**.

In the Countryside

Can you find all these words in the picture below? Write in the correct word against each number. When you have finished you can colour in the picture if you want to.

bridge	stile	mole	ramblers	retriever
fox	flask	badger	wood	rabbit
windmill	footpath	deer	kestrel	stream

1._____   2._____   3._____

4._____   5._____   6._____

7._____   8._____   9._____

10._____   11._____   12._____

13._____   14._____   15._____

© 2006 Stephen Curran

In the High Street

Can you find all these words in the picture below? Write the correct word against each number.

streetlight	**lorry**	**drain**	**butcher**	**road works**
newsagent	**pushchair**	**kerb**	**ironmonger**	**crossing**
greengrocer	**florist**	**bank**	**carrier bag**	**supermarket**

1._____ 2._____ 3._____

4._____ 5._____ 6._____

7._____ 8._____ 9._____

10._____ 11._____ 12._____

13._____ 14._____ 15._____

pinch	acrobat	trapeze
juggler	roller	called
tallest	ballet	kicked
jacket	blackboard	mackintosh

Exercise 62a

1) His favourite _____ programme would be broadcast at 8.00pm.

2) "The performance is about to commence. Would you _____ take your seats."

3) The audience were all looking upwards to see the exciting _____ act.

4) He carried his _____ over his arm in case it rained.

5) He drove along the road _____ searching for the correct address.

6) The postman knocked _____ but no one came to the door.

7) He was the _____ in the class and rose head and shoulders above the rest.

8) The circus _____ kept seven clubs in the air at once.

9) Details of their homework were written on the _____ .

10) He _____ the rugby ball into touch and the game ended.   Score ▱ 10

Exercise 62b

11) It all happened so _____ that it took them by surprise.

12) She was wearing new shoes and they were beginning to _____ her toes.

13) It was their golden wedding anniversary - 50 years of being _____ married.

14) The Bolshoi _____ company performed *Swan Lake* in Moscow.

15) "Answer this question _____ . Have you looked at the answers?"

16) The groundsman used the heavy _____ to flatten the wicket.

17) My hamster is _____ Krusty after the clown in *The Simpsons*.

18) We were entertained by a very skilful _____ 's gymnastic display.

19) His dinner _____ was stained and had to be dry-cleaned.

20) "Put everything back _____ and in the right place."   Score ▱ 10

© 2006 Stephen Curran ae

television	tidily	**Word Bank**
loudly	happily	**TOTAL**
suddenly	slowly	**1,240**
kindly	honestly	

Across

62

3. A video broadcasting system.
5. A large heavy device for flattening lawns.
7. To grip or squeeze something between finger and thumb.
10. Neatly and methodically.
12. A short coat.
13. Joyfully, contentedly, or willingly.
17. Said something in a loud voice.
18. The highest of them all.
19. Fairly or justly, truthfully or genuinely.
20. A horizontal bar between two hanging ropes often used in a circus.

Down

1. Struck with the foot.
2. Not moving quickly.
4. A gymnastic entertainer.
6. Friendly and generous by nature.
8. A raincoat originally made from rubberized fabric.
9. A board of dark colour that is written on with chalk.
11. Noisily.
14. Happening quickly and unexpectedly.
15. A person who can keep several objects in motion in the air at the same time.
16. A form of dance with graceful movements.

Score

/20

Put the mystery letter (✳) into box **62** below. Add in the starred letters from puzzles **63** to **69** then rearrange them to make **Oliver's Mystery Word**.
The clue is **MINERAL**.

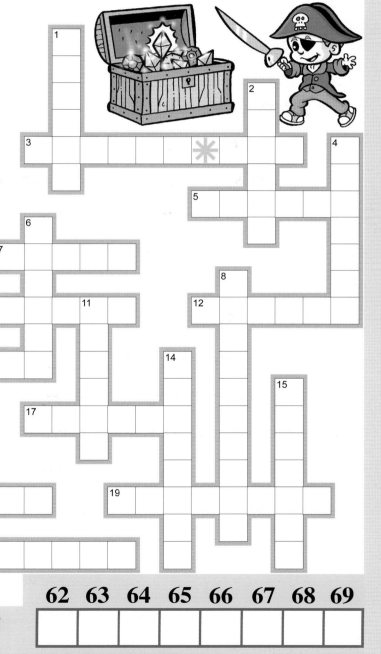

Enter your mystery letters here:

62	63	64	65	66	67	68	69

Now rearrange them:

Mystery Word:

ae © 2006 Stephen Curran

quietly   sadly   gently
poorly   dresses   caravan
roof-rack   sleeping-bag   suitcase
wellington boots sharpened   roared

Across

63

Down

5. Growled loudly.
6. Puts clothes on.
8. Feeling afraid.
10. Having been on many journeys.
11. Hitting hands together quickly and loudly.
13. Become, or make, sharp or sharper.
15. Using little pressure.
17. Container for clothes and other belongings during travel.
18. Making little noise.
19. Spoke to God or some other being.
20. Fabric bag for sleeping in when camping.

1. Loose waterproof rubber boots.
2. Framework for carrying things on the roof of a vehicle.
3. An amount that can be held in the hand.
4. Mobile home designed for towing.
7. Unhappily.
9. Went in.
12. In an inferior or inadequate way.
14. Attached or held firmly.
16. Concentrated on hearing.

© 2006 Stephen Curran

Mystery Letter

Score

20

travelled   listened
entered   fastened
prayed   frightened
handful   clapping

Word Bank
TOTAL
1,260

Exercise 63a

1) It was locked securely with a heavy chain _____ with a large padlock.

2) The monitor had _____ all the pencils in the art room.

3) Last year we stayed in a _____ on a site in the south of France.

4) "Don't be _____ ; it won't hurt you."

5) The robber _____ the shop and demanded money.

6) I had hoped to see her before she left but _____ it wasn't to be.

7) They had _____ a long way and they needed to refuel the car.

8) Only a _____ of volunteers turned up to help unload the lorries.

9) The nurse removed the bandages very _____ to avoid hurting him.

10) He felt very _____ and went to bed with a hot water bottle. **Score** / 10

Exercise 63b

11) "Please open your _____ for inspection," demanded the customs officer.

12) The lion was annoyed and _____ loudly to show its displeasure.

13) "Take off your muddy _____ before you come in."

14) The entire audience were on their feet and _____ in appreciation.

15) In the morning she turned her _____ inside out and hung it up to air.

16) The car was very heavily loaded - even the _____ had suitcases on it.

17) "It's very late. Please be considerate and leave _____ ."

18) She had put out her washing that morning and she _____ it would not rain.

19) He lay awake and _____ to the waves crashing onto the rocks.

20) "I have come to collect the _____ for the bridesmaids." **Score** / 10

ae © 2006 Stephen Curran

hopping	disappointed	queue
yacht	leopard	suite
orchestra	apples	celery
petal	bull	sand-castle

Exercise 64a

1) The prize _____ was a magnificent beast and won first prize at the county show.

2) The circus _____ wore a red jacket, white breeches and black boots.

3) They started to modernise the house by installing a new bathroom _____ .

4) "Would you like _____ or biscuits with your cheese, madam?"

5) It was his ambition to conduct an _____ playing at the Albert Hall.

6) "Get onto the _____ and we'll see if you've lost any weight."

7) I expect she was as _____ as I was that we missed each other.

8) They built a splendid _____ then watched the waves demolish it.

9) She pulled off every _____ from the flower until none was left.

10) The wind changed direction suddenly and the _____ capsized. **Score** ◩ 10

Exercise 64b

11) "Go to the back of the _____ and wait your turn like everyone else!"

12) Whilst on safari our group was fortunate to see a _____ sleeping in the shade.

13) He had many ambitions but his main _____ was to be a professional footballer.

14) Rabbits were _____ away from the cycle track as we approached them.

15) Their music was very good and the _____ beat out a steady rhythm.

16) She put the ice cubes into a polythene bag and used a _____ to crush it.

17) "Golden Delicious are my favourite _____ but my mum prefers Coxes."

18) They had to protect their sandwiches from a _____ that swooped down.

19) We dug a large _____ in the garden and fitted the new pond into it.

20) His eyes were tired and he kept _____ them with his hand. **Score** ◩ 10

  © 2006 Stephen Curran ae

seagull   goal
hole   drummer
ringmaster   rubbing
rolling-pin   scales

Word Bank TOTAL 1,280

Across

64

3. Sailing boat.
5. Not satisfied.
7. Large, spotted African cat.
12. A web-footed white-and-grey sea bird.
13. Large group of musicians.
14. Climbs up a steep incline.
16. A model castle made of damp sand.
17. A kitchen utensil used for rolling out dough and pastry.
19. A hollow space in a solid object.

Down

1. Pressing and moving the hand over the surface of something.
2. Line of people or vehicles waiting.
4. Plural (more than one) of apple.
6. Somebody who plays the drums.
8. Somebody who announces acts and events at a circus.
9. Long-stemmed vegetable with crisp, flattish stems often eaten raw.
10. One of the coloured parts of a flower.
11. Jumping lightly on one foot.
15. Adult male of domestic cattle or other bovine animal.
16. Set of matching furniture.
18. Opening into which a ball or puck must go to score points.

Mystery Letter

Score

20

© 2006 Stephen Curran

swimsuit   toys   bomber
caring   stitches   store
stork   clouds   coins
plumber   matches   wrapped

Across

65

4. To take small quick bites.
5. Things to play with.
8. Hard-backed insect.
10. A large wading bird with long legs.
13. An object for scaring birds away.
15. Resembles or looks like.
19. Knowing something.
20. A shallow pool of water.

Down

1. Somebody who serves at tables.
2. Somebody who installs and repairs water or drainage pipes and fixtures.
3. A place where goods are kept.
6. To cuddle up.
7. Clothing worn for swimming.
9. Lengths of thread to join or decorate material.
11. Showing concern for others.
12. Aircraft designed to carry and drop bombs.
14. Covered up with paper or cloth.
16. Pieces of metal money.
17. Becomes or makes opaque or murky.
18. To walk with short steps causing the body to tilt slightly from side to side.

Mystery Letter

Score / 20

© 2006 Stephen Curran

beetle   nibble
waddle   puddle
snuggle   waiter
scarecrow aware

Word Bank TOTAL 1,300

Exercise 65a

1) "Don't let your little brother play with _____ . He could start a fire."

2) She changed into her _____ before going to paddle in the sea.

3) The squirrel held the nut in his paws and started to _____ it.

4) Her purse was full of change and the _____ were very heavy.

5) The cut was very deep and it needed seven _____ before being dressed.

6) The sandwiches were _____ in silver foil to keep them fresh.

7) Large black _____ were gathering overhead and it looked like rain.

8) In the field the _____ was protecting the crops from the birds.

9) A stag _____ 's long extended jaws are called mandibles.

10) The _____ was shot down but the aircrew survived. **Score** [/ 10]

Exercise 65b

11) My dad called the _____ when we had a burst pipe last winter.

12) "Pull up the covers, _____ down in your bed and keep warm."

13) At the zoo we saw a _____ with a long, straight bill standing on one leg.

14) He didn't so much walk as _____ like a duck along the pavement.

15) My dad uses old jam jars to _____ nails and screws on a shelf in the shed.

16) He had a summer job working as a _____ in the town's finest restaurant.

17) She was _____ of someone behind her and turned to see who it was.

18) It was a very deep _____ and the water came over the top of his boots.

19) "Play nicely together and share your _____ with your friends."

20) The paramedics were _____ for the injured passengers. **Score** [/ 10]

ae © 2006 Stephen Curran

mare	snack	snarl
sneak	sneeze	sniff
snip	snooker	snooze
snorkel	snout	snowman

Exercise 66a

1) The bear bared his teeth and began to _____ angrily.

2) It was very dark in the _____ between the buildings, and dustbins lined the sides.

3) He used his _____ to breathe through as he swam face down in the sea.

4) Her feet were _____ with the cold and she wished she had worn her boots.

5) The racehorse fell at the last fence and its _____ was unseated.

6) She was late and had to _____ back indoors without being heard.

7) Every Wednesday evening they played a few frames of _____ together.

8) The hexagonal paving slabs looked like _____ when they were laid.

9) Pollyanna wore petticoats and long, frilly _____ under her skirt.

10) That evening the _____ had given birth to a foal.

Score [/ 10]

Exercise 66b

11) The terrorists planted a _____ hidden in a holdall but it was defused safely.

12) "Try turning the _____ and see if the door will open."

13) My granddad closed his eyes and had a short _____ after Sunday lunch.

14) The doe lifted her nose to _____ the air in order to detect a predator.

15) Their _____ had stones for his eyes and mouth and a carrot for a nose.

16) A huge pig had his _____ deep in the trough and was eating noisily.

17) He went into hospital to have an operation to remove a _____ stone.

18) She had a small _____ to keep her going until dinner time.

19) "Use this small _____ of material to patch the hole."

20) "Cover your nose if you think you are going to _____ ."

Score [/ 10]

© 2006 Stephen Curran ae

Word Bank

knickers   knob
jockey   alley
kidney   bomb
numb   honeycomb

Word Bank TOTAL 1,320

Across

66

3. Breathing apparatus for swimming just below water.
6. An organ in the abdomen that filters waste liquid.
7. To have a short sleep or nap.
8. With no feeling or sensation.
10. A rider of racehorses.
14. A roughly human figure made from snow.
15. A rounded handle or dial.
16. Adult female horse.
17. To go or act in a stealthy, secretive way.
18. Growl threateningly.
19. To breathe in through the nose.

Down

1. Game played with balls and a cue.
2. A small or narrow street.
4. An animal's nose.
5. A wax structure made of hexagonal (six-sided) cells made by bees.

Down (continued)

9. A missile containing explosive or other destructive material.
11. Panties worn by women and girls.
12. A sudden involuntary expulsion of air through the nose.
13. To cut using small strokes.
17. Small meal.

Mystery Letter

Score / 20

© 2006 Stephen Curran

45

tomb   climber   fluid
cruise   penguin   bully
moist   otter   tramp
wealth   joiner   toilet

Across

(67)

2. A large amount of money or possessions.
4. Utter a roar like a bull.
5. A small European snake with black zigzag pattern on its back.
9. Edible North Atlantic fish related to but smaller than the cod.
12. An aggressive person who mistreats weaker people.
14. Decayed.
15. An aquatic fish-eating mammal with smooth dark brown fur and webbed feet.
16. A seabird that cannot fly.
17. Somebody who climbs rocks or mountains.
19. A bowl-shaped fixture for disposing of bodily waste.
20. A vagrant who has no home and travels on foot.

Down (continued)

10. To travel by sea on a pleasure trip.
11. A grave or burial chamber.
13. A woodworker in the building trade.
18. Slightly wet or damp.

Down

1. A long piece of cloth, often bearing a symbol or slogan, suspended between two poles.
3. Anything liquid.
6. Informal term for father.
7. Social behaviour in terms of what is considered correct or unacceptable.
8. A hut for a dog.

Mystery Letter

Score

/20

46

© 2006 Stephen Curran

Exercise 67a

1) He slipped because the grass was still _____ from the earlier rainfall.

2) He was roped on so when he lost his footing the _____ did not fall.

3) They unfurled a long _____ and draped it across the front of the building.

4) The _____ is the only snake in Britain with a poisonous bite.

5) In the pharaoh's _____ were many valuable treasures to be excavated.

6) He was a man of great _____ with many assets and several properties.

7) Every night my _____ reads my little sister a story before bedtime.

8) From the barn could be heard a loud _____ from the bull.

9) New door frames and window frames were made by the _____ .

10) He built a new _____ for his dog when the old one leaked.   **Score** [/10]

Exercise 67b

11) I love to watch the _____ catching fish that the zookeeper throws to it.

12) "Don't be a _____ Martin, pick on someone your own size!"

13) Mum had cod and chips for supper but Dad had _____ with his chips.

14) The _____ ship called at another port on its voyage around the Mediterranean.

15) It is good _____ to stand back and let others go first.

16) "Would you please put some bleach down the _____ to disinfect it?"

17) Bleach is a very viscous _____ that clings to the inside of the toilet bowl.

18) In its mouth the _____ held a large salmon that it had caught.

19) The floor joists were _____ and had to be replaced.

20) "Don't _____ all over the flower bed, I've just hoed it!"   **Score** [/10]

ae © 2006 Stephen Curran

lorry	ferry	barrow
model	ravel	hostel
tinsel	level	hobby
scrubbing	pram	president

Exercise 68a

1) She felt a _____ of hunger and realised she had not eaten for several hours.

2) The _____ driver had braked on the wet road and his vehicle had jackknifed.

3) "What's your _____ ? I spend my spare time collecting ancient coins."

4) The new tree was not very sturdy so the gardener used a stake to _____ it up.

5) She stood on the windy promenade and could feel the salty _____ on her face.

6) In the _____ was her new baby and they were out for a walk for the first time.

7) At the station the porter used a _____ to carry their cases to the train.

8) "You'll feel a slight _____ ," said the nurse before she gave him the injection.

9) A solitary pale yellow _____ was growing in the rockery.

10) The wind got up and began to _____ her long hair.

Score ⟋ 10

Exercise 68b

11) He had bought a new locomotive for his _____ railway set.

12) I went to the late night _____ to get some cough mixture.

13) His _____ task was to find some wood so that he could light a fire.

14) _____ the fender over the boat's side he slipped and fell into the river.

15) The fairy lights made the _____ on the Christmas tree sparkle.

16) *Do not stop on the _____ crossing'*, said the warning sign.

17) On their cycling holiday they spent the nights at a youth _____ .

18) When _____ of the USA, Abraham Lincoln was assassinated in 1865.

19) She was often on all fours _____ the wooden floors.

20) We took our car to Ireland on the _____ .

Score ⟋ 10

© 2006 Stephen Curran ae

prick	primary
primrose	prop
chemist	pang
flinging	spray

Across

68

2. Cleaning by rubbing hard.
4. An enjoyable activity for pleasure and relaxation.
6. To puncture and make a small hole through the surface.
7. Accommodation for homeless people.
11. A rigid beam, stake, or pole that supports something.
15. To tangle or fray.
16. The first in a sequence, or ranked as most important.
17. A copy of an object usually made on a smaller scale.
18. The head of a state or republic.
19. A boat making regular short river or sea crossings.

Down

1. A jet of fine liquid particles.
3. A shop selling medicines and toiletries.
5. A two-wheeled hand cart.
8. A thin strip of glittering material.
9. Large road vehicle for transporting goods.
10. Not sloping.
12. A spring plant with pale yellow flowers.
13. Throwing violently.
14. A small wheeled vehicle for carrying babies.
16. A short sharp pain.

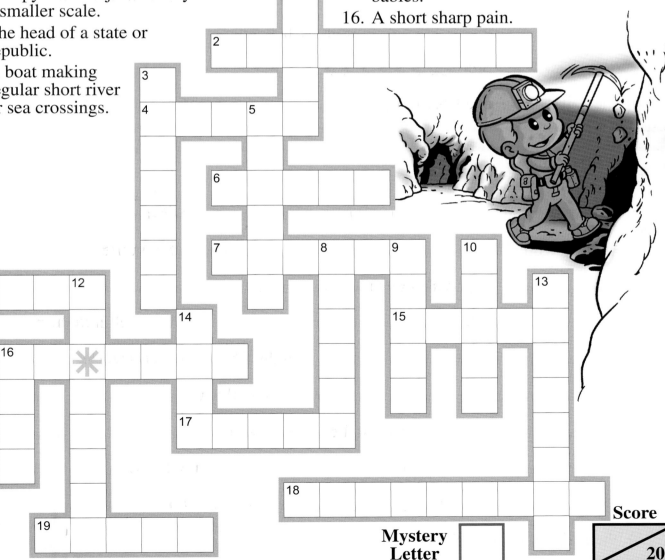

Mystery Letter

Score

20

ae © 2006 Stephen Curran

coy   seventy   eighteen
nineteen   seventeen   stew
brew   sighs   tights
frightening   ledge   budge

Exercise 69a

1) Being born at the beginning of the 20th century he was _____seventy_____ in 1970.

2) She had made a steaming hot Irish _____stew_____ with meat and vegetables.

3) There were encyclopaedias, a dictionary and a thesaurus in the _____bookcase_____ .

4) Soy sauce is dark and salty and made by fermenting _____soya_____ beans in brine.

5) You have to be over _____eighteen_____ to vote in a local or general election.

6) It was a very _____frightening_____ experience and she had nightmares afterwards.

7) The sounds made by the wind as it blew through the trees were like eerie _____sighs_____ .

8) "Make sure the cat doesn't _____tangle_____ my wool while I make myself a cup of tea."

9) "Come away and stop _____spoiling_____ their fun by annoying them."

10) She had to be _____seventeen_____ to drive a car for the first time. **Score** / 10

Exercise 69b

11) She was teasing him by being _____coy_____ and pretending to be shy.

12) He tried with all his might to move it but it just would not _____budge_____ .

13) She had seen _____nineteen_____ different species of bird. One more would make twenty.

14) "Let the tea _____brew_____ for a couple of minutes to bring out the full flavour."

15) The acrobat wore a white singlet, white _____tights_____ and white slippers.

16) The drain was partially blocked with a thick _____sludge_____ and had to be cleaned out.

17) She slipped the solid gold _____bangle_____ over her hand and pushed it up her arm.

18) He desperately _____wanted_____ to go with them but his mother would not let him.

19) They were stuck on a rocky _____ledge_____ and had to wait to be rescued.

20) I helped him to _____achieve_____ success but he took all the credit. **Score** / 10

© 2006 Stephen Curran

sludge
bangle
achieve
spoiling

tangle
bookcase
soya
wanted

Word Bank TOTAL 1,380

Across

(69)

2. To make beer.
4. Breathes long and loud in relief or weariness.
5. To move.
7. Wet material, especially watery snow.
10. One less than 20.
11. Felt a need or desire for something.
13. Pretending to be shy.
14. A jumbled mass of fibres or lines.
15. A rigid bracelet.
16. One more than seventeen.
17. Ten add seven.
18. The soya bean plant.

Down

1. Causing fear or alarm.
3. Damaging or ruining something.
4. The number 70.

Down (continued)

6. A dish of meat, fish or vegetables cooked by slow simmering.
8. A narrow shelf against the wall.
9. A cabinet with shelves for storing books.
12. To succeed in doing or gaining something.
14. A sheer, one-piece, close-fitting garment covering the body from waist to feet.

! Don't forget to go back to page **37** and complete **Oliver's Mystery Word**.

Mystery Letter

Score

20

© 2006 Stephen Curran

Book Three Word List

achieve	blame	cried	felt
acrobat	bless	cries	ferry
actor	blew	cross	few
adder	blue	crow	filled
air	boil	cruise	finch
alive	bomb	crying	firm
alley	bomber	curl	flat
along	bone	daddy	flies
any	bookcase	dance	flinging
anything	bound	dead	flower
apples	bow	death	fluid
arrested	brew	desk	follow
arrived	bright	dew	food
asked	broom	die	football
aware	brown	died	forget
babies	budge	dirt	forgets
ballet	bull	disappointed	fork
bangle	bully	doctor	fresh
banner	bunch	does	frightened
barn	burn	done	frightening
barrow	called	downstairs	garden
basket	caravan	draw	gay
bath	card	dream	gently
beach	caring	dresses	getting
beads	carried	drew	giving
bean	carry	drill	glass
beast	celery	dropped	goal
beat	chemist	dropping	goat
became	cherries	drove	goes
bedroom	cherry	drummer	gone
beetle	church	early	great
before	clapping	east	green
behind	class	easy	grew
bellow	clear	eighteen	haddock
belong	clever	emperor	handful
below	climber	entered	happily
belt	cloud	even	harm
berries	clouds	fail	having
berry	coins	farm	heard
beside	cool	farmer	heat
better	corridor	fastened	heel
bigger	could	fear	hobby
biggest	coy	feast	hole
blackboard	cream	feel	honestly

© 2006 Stephen Curran

Book Three Word List

honeycomb	longest	orchestra	reading
hopping	looked	otter	ready
hostel	looking	outside	rice
hour	lorry	own	riding
hurt	loud	ox	right
iceberg	loudly	oxen	ringmaster
inch	low	pail	roared
inside	mackintosh	pair	roller
jacket	maid	pang	rolling-pin
jelly	manners	party	roof-rack
jockey	many	pass	rotten
join	march	paw	row
joiner	mare	pence	rubbing
jolly	marry	penguin	ruler
juggler	master	petal	running
kennel	matches	pie	sadly
kept	meal	pinch	sail
key	mean	pink	sale
kicked	meat	played	sand-castle
kidney	melt	playground	scales
kindly	merry	please	scarecrow
knew	mice	plumber	scrubbing
knickers	mix	point	seagull
knob	model	pool	seen
know	moist	poorly	seventeen
ladies	nail	pork	seventy
lame	neat	porridge	shade
later	new	pound	shall
lead	next	pram	shame
leaf	nibble	prayed	sharp
lean	night	president	sharpened
learn	nineteen	press	shirt
least	nor	prick	sighs
ledge	north	primary	silk
leopard	note	primrose	sir
less	nothing	prop	skipping
lettuce	numb	puddle	sleeping-bag
level	number	puppy	slippers
lie	oak	queue	slow
lies	off	quietly	slowly
listened	oil	ranch	sludge
living	once	ravel	snack
load	opened	raw	snarl
longer	opening	reach	sneak

ae © 2006 Stephen Curran

Book Three Word List

sneeze	stitches	third	waddle
sniff	stone	those	waiter
snip	stopped	throw	walked
snooker	store	tidily	walking
snooze	stories	tights	wanted
snore	stork	tinsel	warm
snorkel	strawberries	tiny	washed
snout	strong	toilet	wealth
snowman	such	tomb	wellington boots
snuggle	suck	tomorrow	which
some	suddenly	tonight	whip
sound	suitcase	tooth	who
south	suite	town	whole
soya	swimsuit	toys	why
spade	tale	tramp	window
speak	talked	trapeze	within
speaking	talking	travelled	without
spell	tallest	tried	woke
spelling	tame	tries	word
spill	tangle	trip	world
spoiling	teeth	true	worm
spray	television	turn	would
stair	their	two	wrapped
star	these	uncle	wriggle
start	thin	upstairs	wrinkles
stayed	think	use	yacht
stew	thinking	used	yard

Congratulations!

You have now learnt to spell **1,380** words, know what they mean and how to use them in a sentence.

Now move on to **Book 4** to learn lots more words to add to your word bank total.

© 2006 Stephen Curran

Answers

11+ Spelling & Vocabulary
Workbook 3

Exercise 47a
1) farm
2) such
3) bedroom
4) harm
5) shade
6) heat
7) neat
8) garden
9) beat
10) Bless

Exercise 47b
11) less
12) window
13) Press
14) farmer
15) card
16) yard
17) barn
18) broom
19) meat
20) spade

Exercise 48a
1) fear
2) *beast*
3) bunch
4) brown
5) pink
6) glass
7) heard
8) pass
9) clear
10) leaf

Exercise 48b
11) class
12) east
13) town
14) belt
15) flat
16) flower
17) sail
18) think
19) feast
20) pail

Exercise 49a
1) lame
2) spelling
3) drill
4) dream
5) pie
6) tame
7) fail
8) least
9) spill
10) blame

Exercise 49b
11) die
12) shame
13) nail
14) cream
15) meal
16) spell
17) lie
18) pool
19) suck
20) mix

Crossword No. 47

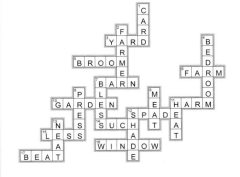

Letter = T

Crossword No. 48

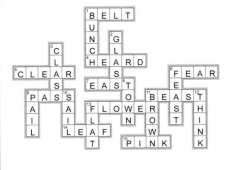

Letter = A

Crossword No. 49

Letter = E

ae © 2006 Stephen Curran

55

11+ Spelling & Vocabulary
Workbook 3

Answers

Exercise 50a
1) death
2) sir
3) oak
4) burn
5) dead
6) ready
7) church
8) third
9) cool
10) shirt

Exercise 50b
11) load
12) goat
13) dirt
14) curl
15) lies
16) Turn
17) firm
18) died
19) hurt
20) food

Exercise 51a
1) crow
2) star
3) upstairs
4) low
5) inside
6) night
7) pair
8) forget
9) slow
10) start

Exercise 51b
11) tonight
12) outside
13) stair
14) word
15) downstairs
16) right
17) air
18) world
19) within
20) bright

Exercise 52a
1) who
2) nor
3) row
4) bow
5) talked
6) walked
7) maid
8) throw
9) why
10) looking

Exercise 52b
11) talking
12) without
13) walking
14) own
15) looked
16) asked
17) sharp
18) which
19) thinking
20) follow

Crossword No. 50

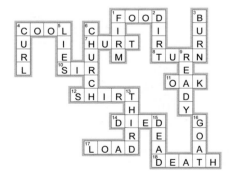

Letter = H

Crossword No. 51

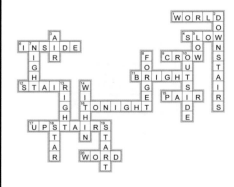

Letter = L

Crossword No. 52

Letter = N

56

© 2006 Stephen Curran

Answers

Exercise 53a
1) filled
2) pork
3) cloud
4) alive
5) north
6) opening
7) along
8) trip
9) doctor
10) speak

Exercise 53b
11) South
12) fork
13) hour
14) loud
15) speaking
16) reading
17) became
18) washed
19) whip
20) opened

Exercise 54a
1) stories
2) teeth
3) tooth
4) babies
5) march
6) green
7) playground
8) football
9) bath
10) having

Exercise 54b
11) ladies
12) giving
13) seen
14) party
15) master
16) living
17) new
18) tiny
19) dance
20) basket

Exercise 55a
1) paw
2) riding
3) jelly
4) carried
5) rice
6) tomorrow
7) merry
8) cherry
9) pence
10) carry

Exercise 55b
11) berries
12) heel
13) shall
14) mice
15) feel
16) jolly
17) once
18) marry
19) cherries
20) berry

Crossword No. 53
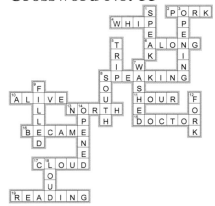

Letter = P

Crossword No. 54
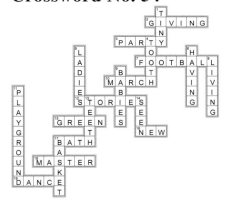

Letter = E

Crossword No. 55

Letter = L

At the Office

1. BRIEFCASE	2. SECRETARY	3. FAN	4. DESK LAMP	5. SKYSCRAPER
6. REPORT	7. POT PLANT	8. FIRST AID KIT	9. LIFT	10. CHART
11. BLIND	12. EXTINGUISHER	13. BIN	14. MANAGER	15. SWIVEL CHAIR

In the Street

1. REMOVAL LORRY	2. CARPORT	3. CHIMNEY	4. BICYCLE	5. SHED
6. HEDGE	7. MOTOR SCOOTER	8. GARAGE	9. LAMP POST	10. 'SOLD' BOARD
11. AERIAL	12. FLOWER BED	13. ROOF	14. BUNGALOW	15. WALL

Answers

Exercise 56a

1) reach
2) raw
3) gay
4) flies
5) please
6) mean
7) easy
8) beads
9) beach
10) cried

Exercise 56b

11) cries
12) warm
13) tried
14) lead
15) great
16) draw
17) bean
18) lean
19) tries
20) crying

Exercise 57a

1) before
2) dropped
3) two
4) slippers
5) getting
6) anything
7) biggest
8) many
9) better
10) below

Exercise 57b

11) skipping
12) felt
13) dropping
14) fresh
15) running
16) any
17) belong
18) stopped
19) their
20) bigger

Exercise 58a

1) melt
2) join
3) kept
4) knew
5) bound
6) few
7) oil
8) sound
9) behind
10) off

Exercise 58b

11) pound
12) boil
13) beside
14) point
15) blew
16) know
17) dew
18) drew
19) nothing
20) grew

Crossword No. 56

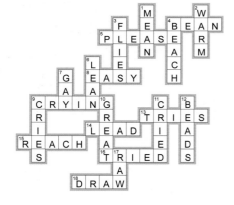

Letter = E

Crossword No. 57

Letter = T

Crossword No. 58

Letter = U

© 2006 Stephen Curran

Answers

Exercise 59a
1) thin
2) use
3) those
4) early
5) oxen
6) could
7) would
8) puppy
9) used
10) later

Exercise 59b
11) ox
12) sale
13) desk
14) these
15) key
16) learn
17) cross
18) strong
19) even
20) *Tale*

Exercise 60a
1) *Blue*
2) does
3) played
4) next
5) goes
6) inch
7) drove
8) note
9) Gone
10) stayed

Exercise 60b
11) whole
12) ruler
13) true
14) woke
15) stone
16) bone
17) done
18) clever
19) Uncle
20) number

Exercise 61a
1) strawberries
2) silk
3) ranch
4) porridge
5) corridor
6) forgets
7) wrinkles
8) lettuce
9) arrested
10) some

Exercise 61b
11) actor
12) longer
13) snore
14) finch
15) longest
16) arrived
17) iceberg
18) worm
19) wriggle
20) Emperor

Crossword No. 59

Letter = E

Crossword No. 60

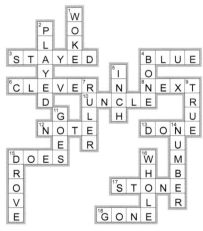

Letter = C

Crossword No. 61

Letter = T

In the Countryside
1. RABBIT	2. FOOTPATH	3. WOOD	4. FOX	5. KESTREL
6. BADGER	7. STILE	8. WINDMILL	9. RETRIEVER	10. STREAM
11. BRIDGE	12. FLASK	13. RAMBLERS	14. DEER	15. MOLE

In the High Street
1. FLORIST	2. DRAIN	3. NEWSAGENT	4. KERB	5. BUTCHER
6. SUPERMARKET	7. CARRIER BAG	8. ROADWORKS	9. GREENGROCER	10. BANK
11. IRONMONGER	12. STREETLIGHT	13. CROSSING	14. PUSHCHAIR	15. LORRY

ae © 2006 Stephen Curran

Answers

Exercise 62a

1) television
2) kindly
3) trapeze
4) mackintosh
5) slowly
6) loudly
7) tallest
8) juggler
9) blackboard
10) kicked

Exercise 62b

11) suddenly
12) pinch
13) happily
14) ballet
15) honestly
16) roller
17) called
18) acrobat
19) jacket
20) tidily

Exercise 63a

1) fastened
2) sharpened
3) caravan
4) frightened
5) entered
6) sadly
7) travelled
8) handful
9) gently
10) poorly

Exercise 63b

11) suitcase
12) roared
13) wellington boots
14) clapping
15) sleeping-bag
16) roof-rack
17) quietly
18) prayed
19) listened
20) dresses

Exercise 64a

1) bull
2) ringmaster
3) suite
4) celery
5) orchestra
6) scales
7) disappointed
8) sand-castle
9) petal
10) yacht

Exercise 64b

11) queue
12) leopard
13) goal
14) hopping
15) drummer
16) rolling-pin
17) apples
18) seagull
19) hole
20) rubbing

Crossword No. 62

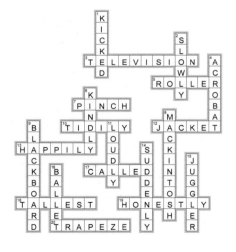

Crossword No. 63

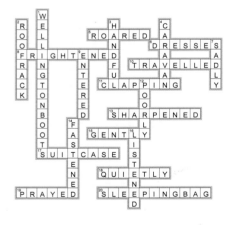

Crossword No. 64

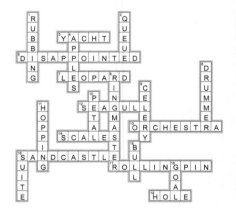

Letter = S

Letter = R

Letter = P

© 2006 Stephen Curran

Answers

Exercise 65a
1) matches
2) swimsuit
3) nibble
4) coins
5) stitches
6) wrapped
7) clouds
8) scarecrow
9) beetle
10) bomber

Exercise 65b
11) plumber
12) snuggle
13) stork
14) waddle
15) store
16) waiter
17) aware
18) puddle
19) toys
20) caring

Exercise 66a
1) snarl
2) alley
3) snorkel
4) numb
5) jockey
6) sneak
7) snooker
8) honeycomb
9) knickers
10) mare

Exercise 66b
11) bomb
12) knob
13) snooze
14) sniff
15) snowman
16) snout
17) kidney
18) snack
19) snip
20) sneeze

Exercise 67a
1) moist
2) climber
3) banner
4) adder
5) tomb
6) wealth
7) daddy
8) bellow
9) joiner
10) kennel

Exercise 67b
11) penguin
12) bully
13) haddock
14) cruise
15) manners
16) toilet
17) fluid
18) otter
19) rotten
20) tramp

Crossword No. 65

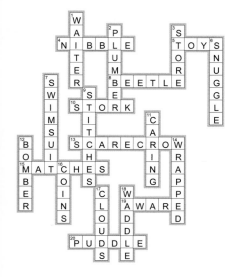

Letter = H

Crossword No. 66

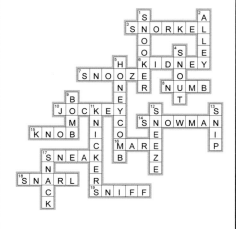

Letter = E

Crossword No. 67

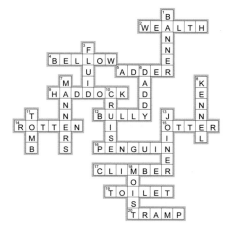

Letter = A

ae © 2006 Stephen Curran

Answers

Exercise 68a

1) pang
2) lorry
3) hobby
4) prop
5) spray
6) pram
7) barrow
8) prick
9) primrose
10) ravel

Exercise 68b

11) model
12) chemist
13) primary
14) Flinging
15) tinsel
16) level
17) hostel
18) president
19) scrubbing
20) ferry

Exercise 69a

1) seventy
2) stew
3) bookcase
4) soya
5) eighteen
6) frightening
7) sighs
8) tangle
9) spoiling
10) seventeen

Exercise 69b

11) coy
12) budge
13) nineteen
14) brew
15) tights
16) sludge
17) bangle
18) wanted
19) ledge
20) achieve

Crossword No. 68

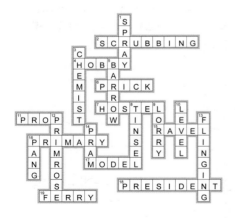

Crossword No. 69

Mystery Word

T A E H L N P E

E L E P H A N T

Mystery Word

L E T U E C T

L E T T U C E

Mystery Word

S R P H E A I P

S A P P H I R E

Letter = I

Letter = P

© 2006 Stephen Curran

PROGRESS CHARTS

Scores

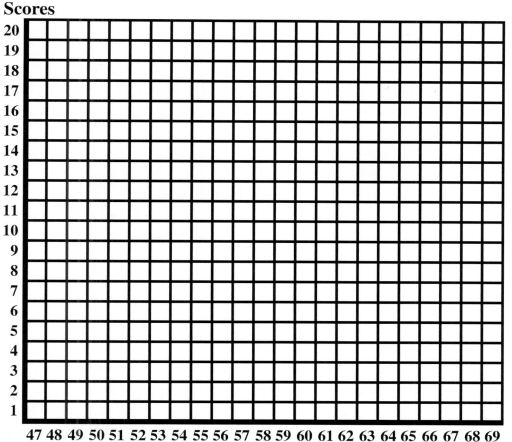

47 48 49 50 51 52 53 54 55 56 57 58 59 60 61 62 63 64 65 66 67 68 69

Exercises

Shade in your score for each exercise on the graph. Add them up for your total score out of 460. Ask an adult to work out the percentage.

Total Score

Percentage

 % **A**

Scores

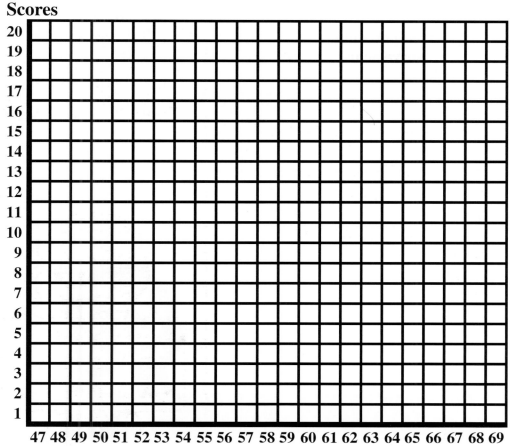

47 48 49 50 51 52 53 54 55 56 57 58 59 60 61 62 63 64 65 66 67 68 69

Crosswords

Shade in your score for each crossword on the graph. Add them up for your total score out of 460.

Total Score

Percentage

 % **B**

For the average percentage add %A and %B and divide by 2

Overall Percentage

%

ae © 2006 Stephen Curran

CERTIFICATE OF

ACHIEVEMENT

This certifies

_____

has successfully completed

11+ Spelling & Vocabulary

WORKBOOK **3**

Overall percentage
score achieved

%

Comment _____

_____

Signed _____
(teacher/parent/guardian)

Date _____